Everybody's Favourite
Christmas Carols

Piano Vocal -Easy Organ

GW00500206

For the first time
arranged for
Piano Vocal – Easy Organ
25 of the World's
best loved
Christmas Carols

including Silent Night
The First Nowell
Away In A Manger
O Come All Ye Faithful and
Good King Wenceslas

Wise Publications
London/New York/Sydney

Exclusively distributed by:

Music Sales Limited
78 Newman Street
London W1

Music Sales Pty. Limited
27 Clarendon Street
Artarmon Sydney
NSW 2064
Australia

Music Sales Corporation
24 East 22nd Street
New York 10010
USA

Contents

Away In A Manger

(For Organ: Registration No. 7)

3.   Be near me, Lord Jesus;
       I ask Thee to stay
       Close by me forever,
       And love me, I pray.
       Bless all the dear children
       In Thy tender care,
       And fit us for heaven,
       To live with Thee there.

Silent Night

(For Organ: Registration No. 7)

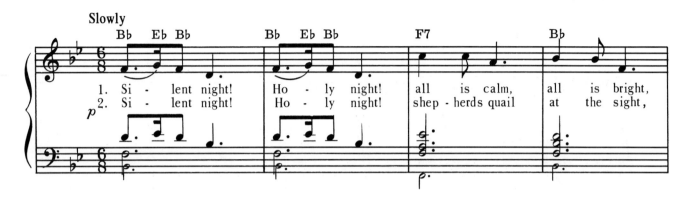

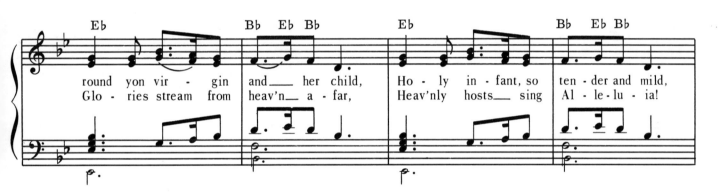

3. Silent night! holy night!
   Son of God, love's pure light;
   Radiant beams Thy holy face
   With the dawn of saving grace,
   Jesus, Lord, at Thy birth,
   Jesus, Lord, at Thy birth.

First Nowell (The)

(For Organ: Registration No. 4)

3. And by the light of that same star,
   Three wise men came from country far;
   To seek for a king was their intent,
   And to follow the star wherever it went.
   Nowell etc.

4. This star drew nigh to the north-west,
   O'er Bethlehem it took its rest,
   And there it did both stop and stay,
   Right over the place where Jesus lay.
   Nowell etc.

5. Then let us all with one accord,
   Sing praises to our heavenly Lord,
   That hath made heaven and earth of nought,
   And with His blood mankind hath bought.
   Nowell etc.

God Rest You Merry Gentlemen

(F or Organ: Registration No. 2)

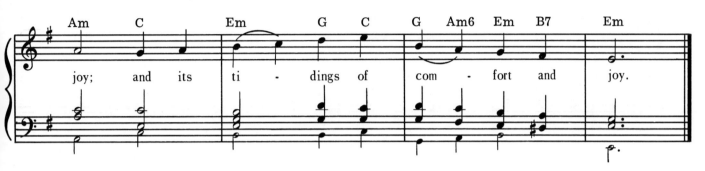

3. Go, fear not, said God's Angels,
   Let nothing you affright,
   For there is born in Bethlehem,
   Of a pure Virgin bright,
   One able to advance you,
   And throw down Satan quite.
       And its tidings etc.

4. The shepherds at those tidings,
   Rejoiced much in mind,
   And left their flocks a-feeding
   In tempest storms of wind,
   And straight they came to Bethlehem,
   The son of God to find.
       And its tidings etc.

5. Now when they came to Bethlehem,
   Where our sweet Saviour lay,
   They found him in a manger,
   Where oxen feed on hay,
   The blessed Virgin kneeling down,
   Unto the Lord did pray.
       And its tidings etc.

6. With sudden joy and gladness
   The shepherds were beguil'd,
   To see the babe of Israel
   Before His mother mild.
   On them with joy and cheerfulness
   Rejoice each mother's child.
       And its tidings etc.

7. Now to the Lord sing praises,
   All you within this place;
   Like we true loving brethren,
   Each other to embrace,
   For the merry time of Christmas
   Is drawing on apace.
       And its tidings etc.

Once In Royal David's City

(For Organ: Registration No. 3)

3. And through all His wondrous childhood,
   He would honour and obey,
   Love and watch the lowly Maiden
   In whose gentle arms He lay;
   Christian children all must be
   Mild, obedient, good as He.

4. For He is in our childhood's pattern,
   Day by day like us He grew;
   He was little, weak and helpless,
   Tears and smiles like us He knew;
   And He feeleth for our sadness,
   And He shareth in our gladness.

5. And our eyes at last shall see Him,
   Through His own redeeming love,
   For that Child so dear and gentle
   Is our Lord in heaven above;
   And he leads His children on
   To the place where He is gone.

6. Not in that poor lowly stable,
   With the oxen standing by,
   We shall see Him; but in heaven,
   Set at God's right hand on high;
   When like stars his children crown'd
   All in white shall wait around.

I Saw Three Ships

(For Organ: Registration No. 6)

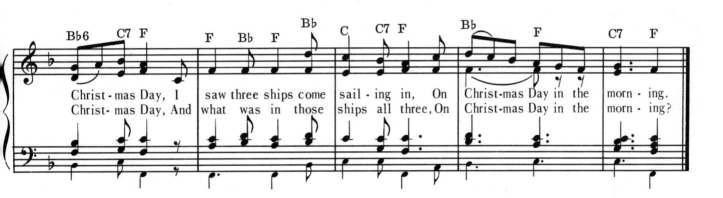

3. The Virgin Mary and Christ were there,
On Christmas day, on Christmas day:
The Virgin Mary and Christ were there,
On Christmas day in the morning.

4. Pray, whither sailed those ships all three,
On Christmas day, on Christmas day?
Pray whither sailed those ships all three,
On Christmas day in the morning?

5. O they sailed into Bethlehem,
On Christmas day, on Christmas day;
O they sailed into Bethlehem,
On Christmas day in the morning.

6. And all the bells on earth shall ring,
On Christmas day, on Christmas day;
And all the bells on earth shall ring,
On Christmas day in the morning.

7. And all the Angels in heaven shall sing,
On Christmas day, on Christmas day;
And all the Angels in heaven shall sing,
On Christmas day in the morning.

8. And all the souls on earth shall sing,
On Christmas day, on Christmas day;
And all the souls on earth shall sing,
On Christmas day in the morning.

9. Then let us all rejoice again,
On Christmas day, on Christmas day;
Then let us all rejoice amain,
On Christmas day in the morning.

O Come All Ye Faithful

(For Organ: Registration No. 4)

3. Sing, choirs of Angels,
   Sing in exultation,
   Sing, all ye citizens of heav'n above:
   'Glory to God in the highest;'
      O come, let us etc.

4. Yea, Lord, we greet Thee,
   Born this happy morning;
   Jesu, to Thee be glory given;
   Word of the Father, Now in flesh appearing;
      O come, let us etc.

Good Christian Men Rejoice

(For Organ: Registration No. 2)

3. Good Christian men, rejoice
With heart and soul and voice;
Now ye need not fear the grave:
Peace! Peace!
Jesus Christ was born to save!
Calls you one and calls you all,
To gain His everlasting hall:
Christ was born to save!
Christ was born to save!

Joy To The World

(For Organ: Registration No. 3)

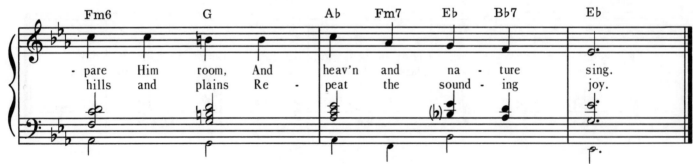

3. No more let sins and sorrows grow,
    Nor thorns infest the ground;
    He comes to make His blessings flow
    Far as the curse is found.

4. He rules the world with truth and grace,
    And makes the nations prove
    The glories of His righteousness,
    And wonders of His love.

Unto Us A Boy Is Born

(For Organ: Registration No. 4)

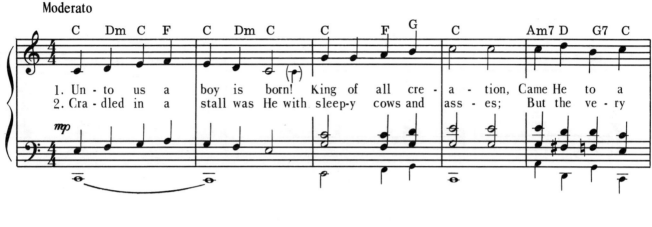

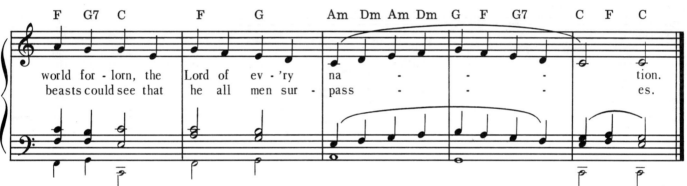

3. Herod then with fear was filled:
"A prince", he said, "in Jewry!"
All the little boys he killed
At Bethlem in his fury.

4. Now may Mary's son, who came
So long ago to love us,
Lead us all with hearts aflame
Unto the joys above us.

5. Omega and Alpha he!
Let the organ thunder,
While the choir with peals of glee
Doth rend the air asunder.

O Little Town Of Bethlehem

(For Organ: Registration No. 3)

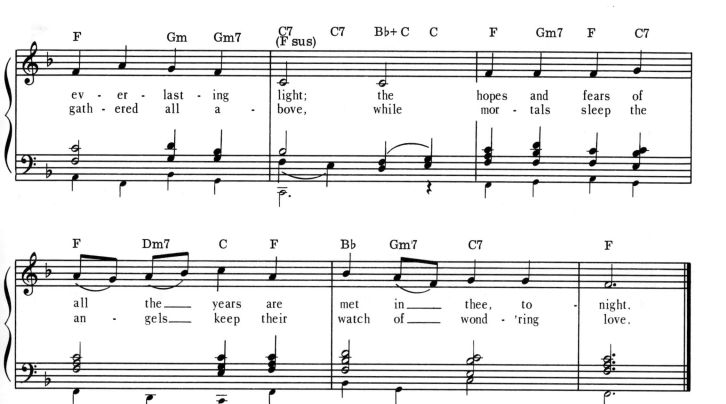

3. How silently, how silently,
The wondrous gift is given!
So God imparts to human hearts
The blessings of His heaven.
No ear may hear His coming;
But in this world of sin,
Where meek souls will receive Him, still
The dear Christ enters in.

4. Where children pure and happy
Pray to the blessed Child,
Where misery cries out to Thee,
Son of the mother mild;
Where charity stands watching
And faith holds wide the door,
The dark night wakes the glory breaks,
And Christmas comes once more.

5. O holy child of Bethlehem,
Descend to us we pray;
Cast out our sin and enter in,
Be born in us today.
We hear the Christmas Angels
The great glad tidings tell:
O come to us, abide with us,
Our Lord Emmanuel.

Hark The Herald Angels Sing

(For Organ: Registration No. 5)

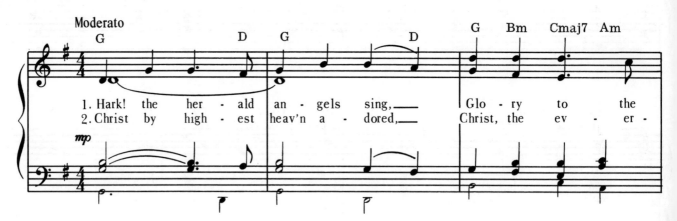

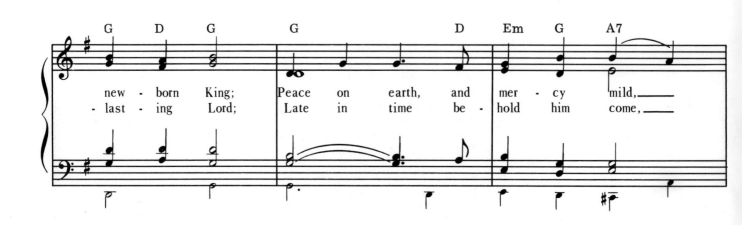

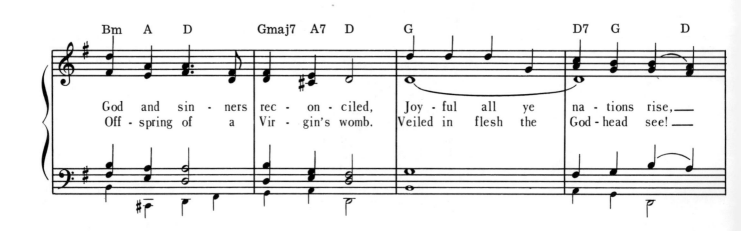

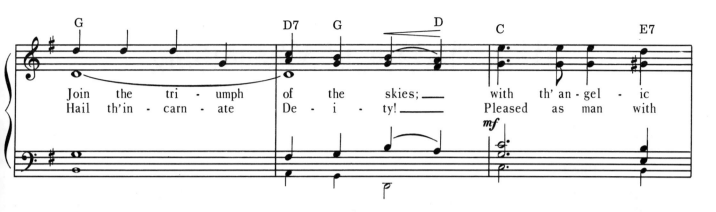

Join the tri - umph of the skies; ___ with th' an - gel - ic
Hail th'in - carn - ate De - i - ty! ___ Pleased as man with

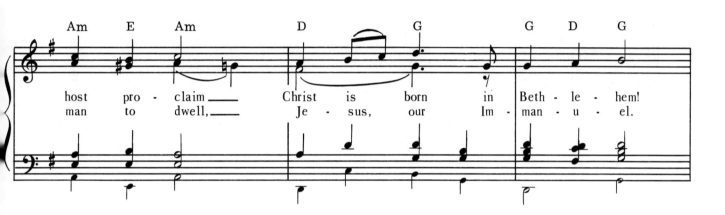

host pro - claim ___ Christ is born in Beth - le - hem!
man to dwell, ___ Je - sus, our Im - man - u - el.

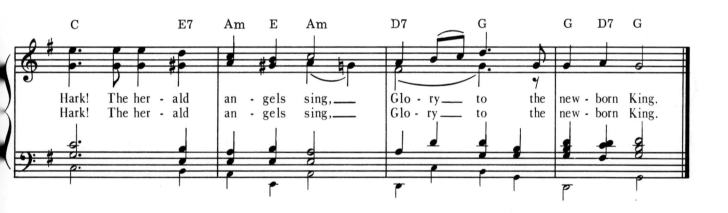

Hark! The her - ald an - gels sing, ___ Glo - ry ___ to the new - born King.
Hark! The her - ald an - gels sing, ___ Glo - ry ___ to the new - born King.

3. Hail, the heaven born Prince of peace!
    Hail, the Son of righteousness!
    Light and life to all He brings,
    Risen with healing in His wings,
    Mild He lays His glory by;
    Born that man no more may die;
    Born to raise the sons of earth;
    Born, to give them second birth.
        Hark! the herald angels sing,
        Glory to the new-born King!

Here We Come A Wassailing

(For Organ: Registration No. 2)

3. Good Master and good Mistress,
   As you sit by the fire,
   Pray think of us poor children
   Who are wand'ring in the mire.
       Love and joy etc.

4. God bless the Master of this house,
   Likewise the Mistress too;
   And all the little children
   That round the table go.
       Love and joy etc.

Twelve Days Of Christmas

(For Organ: Registration No. 5)

Mistletoe Bough (The)

(For Organ: Registration No. 1)

3. They sought her that night and they sought her next day,
    And they sought her again when a week passed away;
    In the highest, the lowest, the loneliest spot
    Young Lovel sought wildly but found her not.
    And years flew by and their grief at last
    Was told as a sorrowful tale long past;
    And when Lovel appeared the children cried,
    "See, the old man weeps for his fairy bride."
        Oh! the mistletoe bough etc.

4. At length, an oak chest that long had laid hid
    Was found in the castle; they raised the lid,
    And a skeleton form lay mouldering there
    In the bridal wreath of the lady fair.
    Oh! sad was her fate! In sportive jest,
    She hid from her lord in the old oak chest;
    It closed with a spring and her bridal bloom
    Lay gathering there in a living tomb.
        Oh! the mistletoe bough etc.

Ding Dong Merrily On High

(For Organ: Registration No. 2)

3. Ring out, merry merry bells,
The Angels all are singing.
Ding dong! swing the steep bells,
Sound joyous news we're bringing!
   Gloria etc.

4. Hark now! happily we sing,
The Angels wish us merry!
Ding dong! dancing as we bring
Good news from Virgin Mary.
   Gloria etc.

Angels From The Realms Of Glory

(For Organ: Registration No. 3)

Fairly slow

1. An - gels, from the realms of glo - ry Wing your flight o'er
2. Shep - herds in the fields a - bi - ding, Watch - ing o'er your

all the earth; Ye who sang cre - a - tion's sto - ry, Now pro - claim Mes -
flocks by night; God with man is now re - si - ding; Yon - der shines the

CHORUS

- si - ah's birth. Come and wor - ship, wor - ship Christ the new - born King.
in - fant light.

3. Sages leave your contemplations,
Brighter visions beam afar;
Seek the great desire of nations,
Ye have seen His natal star.
Come and worship etc.

4. Saints, before the altar bending
Watching long with hope and fear,
Suddenly the Lord, descending,
In His temple shall appear;
Come and worship etc.

5. Sinner, wrung with true repentance,
Doomed for guilt to endless pains,
Justice now revokes the sentence –
Mercy calls you – break your chains.
Come and worship etc.

We Wish You A Merry Christmas

(For Organ: Registration No. 6)

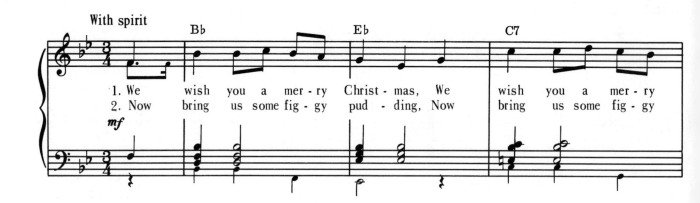

1. We wish you a mer-ry Christ-mas, We wish you a mer-ry
2. Now bring us some fig-gy pud-ding, Now bring us some fig-gy

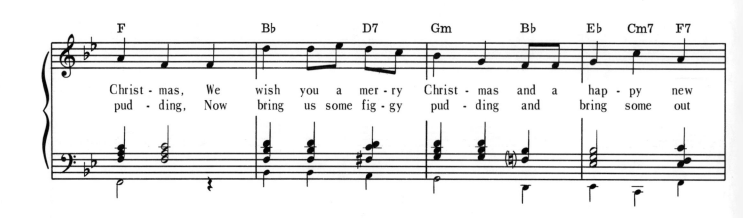

Christ-mas, We wish you a mer-ry Christ-mas and a hap-py new
pud-ding, Now bring us some fig-gy pud-ding and bring some out

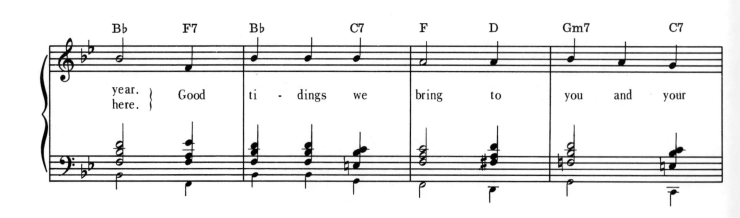

year.
here. } Good ti-dings we bring to you and your

3. For we all like figgy pudding,
   For we all like figgy pudding,
   For we all like figgy pudding,
   So bring some out here.
       Good tidings etc.

4. And we won't go till we've got some,
   And we won't go till we've got some,
   And we won't go till we've got some,
   So bring some out here.
       Good tidings etc,

Hark How All The Welkin Rings

(For Organ: Registration No. 2)

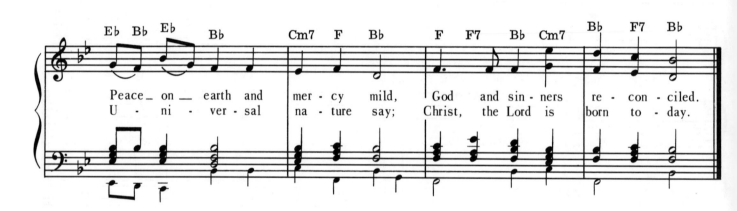

3. Christ, by highest heav'n adored,
    Christ, the everlasting Lord;
    Late in time behold Him come,
    Offspring of a Virgin's womb.

4. Veiled in flesh, the Godhead see!
    Hail the incarnate Deity!
    Pleased as man with men to appear,
    Jesus, our Emmanuel here!

5. Hail the heav'nly Prince of peace!
    Hail the Sun of righteousness!
    Light and life to all He brings,
    Risen with healing in His wings.

Holly And The Ivy

(For Organ: Registration No. 4)

1. The holly and the ivy, When they are both full grown, of all the trees that are
2. The holly bears a blossom, as white as the lily flower, and Mary bore sweet

in the wood, the holly bears the crown;
Jesus Christ, to be our sweet saviour.

CHORUS

The rising of the sun and the running of the deer, The playing of the merry organ, sweet singing in the choir,

3. The holly bears a berry,
As red as any blood,
And Mary bore sweet Jesus Christ
To do poor sinners good.
The rising of etc.

4. The holly bears a prickle,
As sharp as any thorn,
And Mary bore sweet Jesus Christ
On Christmas day in the morn.
The rising of etc.

5. The holly bears a bark,
As bitter as any gall,
And Mary bore sweet Jesus Christ
For to redeem us all.
The rising of etc.

6. The holly and the ivy,
When they are both full grown,
Of all the trees that are in the wood,
The holly bears the crown.
The rising of etc.

Good King Wenceslas

(For Organ: Registration No. 5)

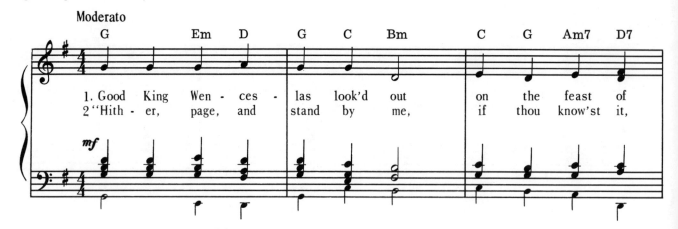

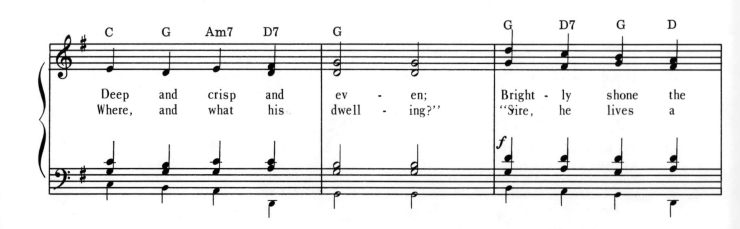

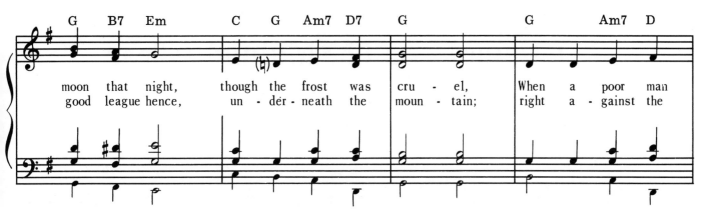

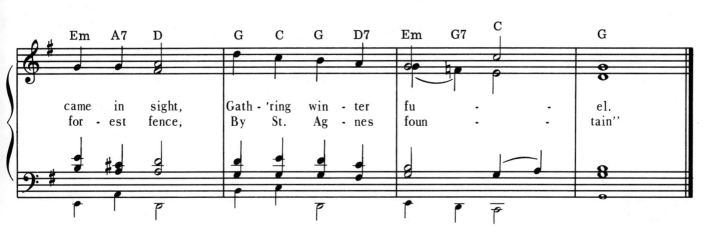

3. "Bring me flesh and bring me wine,
    Bring me pine logs hither;
    Thou and I will see him dine,
    When we bear them thither."
    Page and monarch forth they went,
    Onward both together,
    Through the rude winds wild lament,
    And the bitter weather.

4. "Sire, the night is darker now
    And the wind blows stronger;
    Fails my heart, I know not how,
    I can go no longer."
    "Mark my footsteps, good my page!
    Tread thou in them boldly;
    Thou shall find the winter's rage
    Freeze thy blood less coldly."

5. In his master's steps he trod,
    Where the snow lay dinted;
    Heat was in the very sod
    Which the saint had printed.
    Therefore, Christian men, be sure —
    Wealth or rank possessing —
    Ye, who now will bless the poor,
    Shall yourselves find blessing.

It Came Upon The Midnight Clear

(For Organ: Registration No. 3)

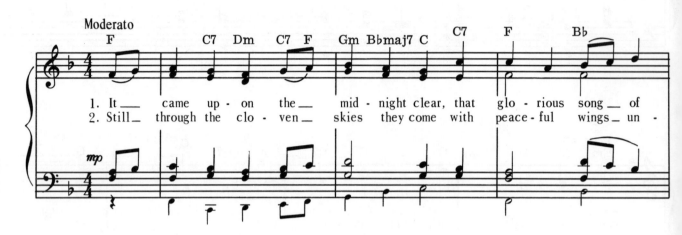

1. It came up - on the mid - night clear, that glo - rious song of
2. Still through the clo - ven skies they come with peace - ful wings un -

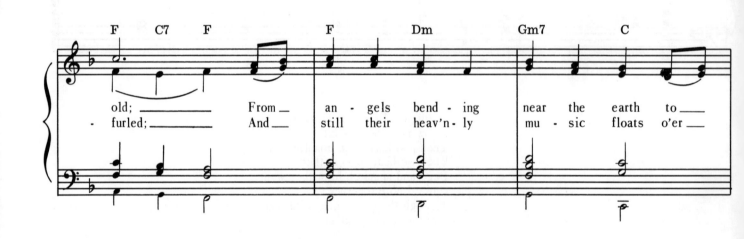

old; From an - gels bend - ing near the earth to
-furled; And still their heav'n - ly mu - sic floats o'er

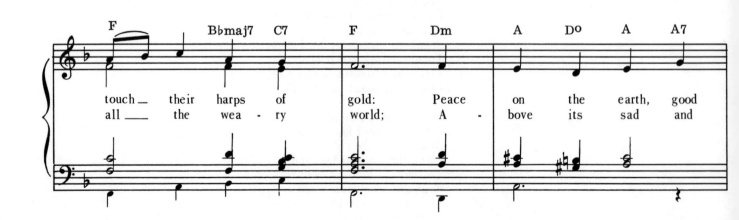

touch their harps of gold: Peace on the earth, good
all the wea - ry world; A - bove its sad and

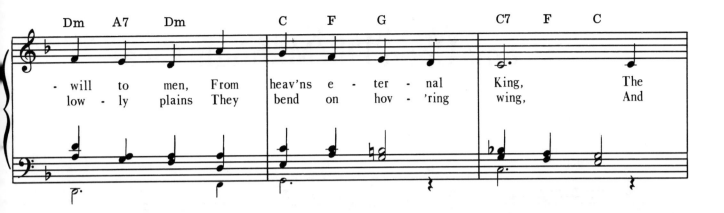

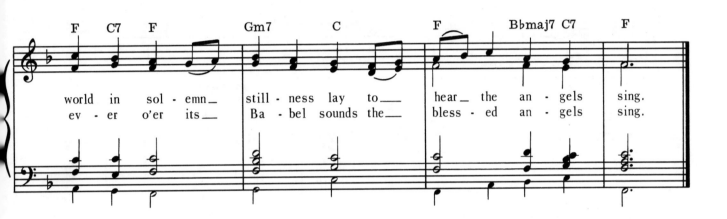

3. Yet with the woes of sin and strife
    The world has suffered long;
    Beneath the Angel-strain have rolled
    Two thousand years of wrong;
    And men, at war with men, hear not
    The love-song which they bring;
    Oh! hush the noise, ye men of strife
    And hear the angels sing!

4. And ye, beneath life's crushing load,
    Whose forms are bending low,
    Who toil along the climbing way
    With painful steps and slow,
    Look now! for glad and golden hours
    Come swiftly on the wing;
    O rest beside the weary road
    And hear the Angels sing!

We Three Kings

(For Organ: Registration No. 4)

(CASPAR)

3. Frankincense to offer have I;
    Incense owns a Deity nigh:
    Prayer and praising, all men raising,
    Worship him, God most high.
    O star of wonder etc.

(BALTHASAR)

4. Myrrh is mine; its bitter perfume
    Breathes a life of gathering gloom;
    Sorrowing, sighing, bleeding, dying,
    Sealed in the stone - cold tomb.
    O star of wonder etc.

(ALL)

5. Glorious now, behold him arise,
    King and God and Sacrifice!
    Heaven sings alleluya,
    Alleluya the earth replies.
    O star of wonder etc.

While Shepherds Watched Their Flocks

(For Organ: Registration No. 3)

3. "To you in David's town this day
   Is born of David's line
   A Saviour, who is Christ the Lord;
   And this shall be the sign:

4. "The heavenly Babe you there shall find
   To human view displayed,
   All meanly wrapped in swathing bands
   And in a manger laid!"

5. Thus spake the Seraph; and forthwith
   Appeared a shining throng
   Of Angels praising God, who thus
   Addressed their joyful song:

6. "All glory be to God on high,
   And on the earth be peace;
   Good-will henceforth from heaven to men
   Begin and never cease."

Christians Awake

(For Organ: Registration No. 6)

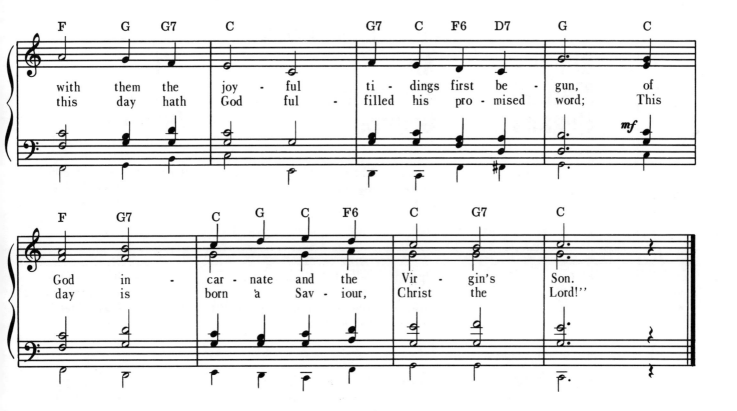

3. To Bethlehem straight the enlightened shepherds ran
    To see the wonder God had wrought for man,
    And found, with Joseph and the Blessed Maid,
    Her Son, the Saviour, in a manger laid:
    Then to their flocks, still praising God, return,
    And their glad hearts with holy rapture burn.

4. O may we keep and ponder in our mind
    God's wondrous love in saving lost mankind;
    Trace we the Babe, Who hath retrieved our loss,
    From His poor manger to His bitter Cross;
    Tread in His steps, assisted by His Grace,
    Till man's first heavenly state again takes place.

5. Then may we hope, the Angelic hosts among,
    To sing, redeemed, a glad triumphal song;
    He that was born upon this joyful day
    Around us all His glory shall display;
    Saved by his love, incessant we shall sing
    Eternal praise to heaven's Almighty King.

Registration No.	*Single - Manual Organs	*All Electronic Organs		*All Drawbar Organs	
1	8' 4' I II III	Upper: Lower: Pedal:	Flute 8' Melodia 8' 8', Soft	Upper: Lower: Pedal:	60 8808 000 (00) 5554 433 (1) 4-2 (Spinet 3)
2	8' I II	Upper: Lower: Pedal:	Cello 16', Trumpet 8', Flute 8', 4' Reed 8', Viola 8' (String 8') 16', 8', Full	Upper: Lower: Pedal:	40 8606 005 (00) 4543 222 (1) 4-2 (Spinet 3)
3	8' 2' I III V	Upper: Lower: Pedal:	Flute 16', (Tibia 16'), Clarinet 8', (Reed 8') Diapason 8' 16', Soft	Upper: Lower: Pedal:	60 8805 005 (00) 5544 321 (0) 4-2 (Spinet 3)
4	8' 4' 2' I II III V	Upper: Lower: Pedal:	Flute 16', (Tibia 16'), Flute 8' Diapason 8', Melodia 8' 16', 8' Medium	Upper: Lower: Pedal:	80 8080 800 (00) 6544 444 (2) 4-2 (Spinet 3)
5	8' 4' II	Upper: Lower: Pedal:	Flute 16', (Tibia 16'), Flute 8', Reed 8', Horn 8' Melodia 8', Diapason 8' 16', 8' Full	Upper: Lower: Pedal:	50 8806 006 (00) 5555 443 (3) 4-2 (Spinet 3)
6	8' 4' 2' I II V	Upper: Lower: Pedal:	Flute 16', (Tibia 16'), Flute 8', 4' Diapason 8', Horn 8' 16', 8' Medium	Upper: Lower: Pedal:	00 8080 600 (00) 4433 222 (0) 4-2 (Spinet 3)
7	8' II IV V	Upper: Lower: Pedal:	Diapason 8' Flute 8' 8' Medium	Upper: Lower: Pedal:	60 8008 000 (00) 5544 000 (0) 4-2 (Spinet 3)

* Vibrato and Reverberation left to personal preference

Printed in England by WEST CENTRAL PRINTING CO. LTD., London and Suffolk.